The Forty-Niners

The Story of the California Gold Rush

Cynthia Mercati

Perfection Learning®

Cover & Inside Illustration: Dan Hatala
Designer: Emily J. Greazel

Image Credits: ArtToday (some images copyright www.arttoday.com) pp. 4, 6, 7, 8 (top), 9, 14, 15, 16, 17, 20, 21, 28, 32, 33, 37, 42, 46, 52; Corel Professional Photo p. 23; Courtesy, Colorado Historical Society F11878 p. 22; Courtesy, Colorado Historical Society F12300 p. 25; Courtesy, Colorado Historical Society F7920 p. 44; California History Section, California State Library pp. 11, 18, 31, 53; The Bancroft Library, University of California pp. 8 (bottom), 38.

About the Author

Cynthia Mercati is a writer and a professional actress. She has written many plays for a children's theatre that tours and performs at various schools. She also appears in many of the plays herself.

Ms. Mercati loves reading about history and visiting historical places. When she writes a historical play or book, she wants her readers to feel like they are actually living the story.

Ms. Mercati also loves baseball. Her favorite team is the Chicago White Sox. She grew up in Chicago, Illinois, but she now lives in Des Moines, Iowa. Ms. Mercati has two children and one dog.

Printed in the United States of America. For information, contact Perfection Learning® Corporation, 1000 North Second Avenue, P.O. Box 500, Logan, Iowa 51546-0500.
Tel: 1-800-831-4190 • Fax: 1-800-543-2745
perfectionlearning.com
PB ISBN-10: 0-7891-2493-9 ISBN-13: 978-0-7891-2493-7
RLB ISBN-10: 0-7569-0303-3 ISBN-13: 978-0-7569-0303-9
4 5 6 7 8 9 PP 13 12 11 10 09 08

Contents

In the days of old,
  in the days of gold,
How often I repine,
For the days of old,
  when we dug up the gold
In the days of '49.

Chorus from the traditional song "The Days of '49"

Chapter

Big News

I was one of the forty-niners. You don't know what a forty-niner was, do you?

We were the folks who rushed off to California in 1849 to search for gold. More than 100,000 of us traveled west.

Most of us were men. We had lots of adventures. We had many hardships too.

My name is Andy Farrell. My pa's name is Eli Farrell. I have a ma. I also have a little sister, Mary Jane.

We lived in a small town in Massachusetts. Pa ran a livery stable. That's a place where horses are kept.

My story starts when I was 12 years old. That's when Pa and I took off to look for gold. But the story of the gold rush really began earlier.

In 1838, John Sutter came to California from Switzerland. That's a country in Europe. California belonged to Mexico then.

In 1840, Sutter got a **land grant** from the Mexican government. He built Sutter's Fort on this land.

John Sutter

By 1848, Sutter's Fort was a busy place. It had orchards, a **tannery**, **warehouses**, and a **flour mill**.

Sutter's Fort

James Marshall

Sutter decided he needed a **sawmill**. He hired a carpenter to build it. The carpenter's name was James Marshall.

Sutter wanted his sawmill built where the American and Sacramento Rivers met.

Sutter's mill

Gold nugget

On January 24, 1848, Marshall was walking by a ditch that carried water from the river to the sawmill. He saw some shiny pebbles at the bottom of the ditch. He picked up one. The soft pebble was a yellow color.

Marshall's heart beat faster. Could this little yellow stone be gold?

Marshall remembered hearing that gold was soft. He bit the pebble. His teeth left marks.

Then Marshall pounded the pebble. It bent. But it didn't break.

Now Marshall was sure. He had discovered gold!

Marshall told Sutter about his discovery.

Sutter made Marshall and his workmen promise not to say anything about the gold for six weeks. Sutter promised that they would all share it equally if they kept the secret.

But it was Sutter who couldn't keep quiet. Less than a week after the discovery, he wrote to a friend. In the letter, he told all about finding gold.

Sutter's friend told others. Within three months, everyone in California knew about the gold strike.

In August, the *New York Herald* newspaper printed the story. Soon, news of the discovery spread throughout the country. Then it spread throughout the world.

The gold rush was on!

James Marshall's drawing of his gold discovery

2

Chapter

The Argonauts

Back East, we heard that the hills in California were lined with gold. The stories said that the riverbeds were filled with gold **nuggets**. They were the size of eggs.

Pa knew most of these rumors were **tall tales**. But still, he wanted to be a part of the gold rush.

"I want to fill my pockets with some of that gold," Pa told Ma. "Andy and I will head to California first. When we make enough money, we'll send for you and Mary Jane."

Ma thought looking for gold was a foolish idea. But Pa put his foot down.

"This is our big chance to strike it rich," he said. "I'm going!"

Pa sold the livery stable. That's how he got the money for our trip.

Ma and Mary Jane moved in with my grandparents. It was hard to say good-bye to them. But it was exciting to think about where I was going.

Lots of people had to travel to the goldfields in covered wagons. But if you lived in the East, you could go by ship. That's what Pa and I did.

There were two ways to sail to California. The safe way was to go around South America by way of Cape Horn. But that was also the long way.

The faster route was by way of Panama. But that was also the more dangerous way.

Pa wanted to get to the goldfields quickly. So we boarded a ship in New York City bound for Panama. The ship was full **to the gills** with men heading off to search for gold. The trip took about three weeks.

We all got off the boat at Chagres, Panama. There, we had to pay boatmen to take us up the Chagres River. We went in long canoes called *bungos*. The trip took three days.

Chagres River

Chagres jungle

We finally reached Cruces, a small village. From there, we had to make our way through the jungle. We paid six dollars to travel in an oxcart.

The weather was steaming hot. It rained every day.

My body felt like it was on fire. Armies of insects crawled over my skin.

The drinking water was bad. Lots of gold hunters got sick. A great number of them died. I was glad I was young and strong.

The jungle was dangerous. But it was also full of interesting sights. Everywhere there were brightly colored birds, strange animals, and long, slithery snakes.

We reached Panama City several days later. We had to wait a week for a ship to take us to California.

Luckily, we had bought our tickets in New York for this part of the trip. Some people hadn't. They had to wait weeks, sometimes months, before they could buy one in Panama.

The second ship was even more crowded than the first one. It was full of hot-blooded men who couldn't wait to start looking for gold.

Jason and the Argonauts

These men were tired of traveling. They were tired of eating bad food. The whole ship was boiling over with bad tempers. Fights broke out over the smallest things.

Those of us who went by sea to hunt for gold were nicknamed *Argonauts*. The name came from the Greek **myth** about Jason. Jason's ship was called the *Argo*. The men who sailed with him were Argonauts. They also searched for a treasure—the Golden Fleece.

Pa and I were two mighty tired Argonauts when our ship dropped anchor in California. We were mighty excited too.

With big eyes, I looked across the water to the city of San Francisco. It was no more than a **hodgepodge** of shacks. Everything looked like it had been put up overnight.

But beyond that wild town lay the goldfields—and our fortune!

San Francisco Bay

Chapter

Shirttail Hill

San Francisco was jammed with forty-niners. They had come from all corners of the United States.

Many had come from farther away too. Some came from Italy, Germany, Argentina, and Peru. Some were Mexicans in **serapes**. Others were Chinese in jackets and **pantaloons**.

Men of all nations crowded the city. The streets seemed to echo with a hundred different languages!

But all of us had one thing in common. We were all after gold.

Tools

The first thing Pa did was buy tools for gold hunting. He bought food too.

Everything in San Francisco cost a bundle of money. Eggs were $10 a dozen. Flour was $50 a barrel. A new shirt was $40!

Not just the miners wanted to strike it rich. The store owners and farmers did too. That's why they'd raised their prices so high.

After we had our supplies, Pa and I set out for the goldfields. We bought passage on a **steamer**. It took us to Sacramento.

From there, we hiked. We carried all of our belongings in packs on our backs.

We were on our way to Shirttail Hill. A man on the boat to Panama had told Pa he'd heard the gold was thick there.

Wherever gold had been discovered, a camp had sprung up. We passed a heap of them on our way to Shirttail Hill.

The camps all had funny names—Bedbug, Ten-Cent Gulch, Mule Diggings, and Grizzly Flat.

Up hills and through valleys, Pa and I walked on. I kept a lookout for any gold  nuggets that might be lying around. But I didn't see any.

The only trees were evergreens. The sun blazed high during the day. At night, cold set in.

Pa and I ate hunks of bread and slabs of bacon. I sure did miss Ma's cooking.

After three days of walking, Pa and I came to Shirttail Hill. It looked just like all the other camps.

Makeshift camp

A jumble of tents and shacks overlooked a creek. Trash littered the road that ran from the town down to the gold diggings.

Pa set up our tent. But my heart was too heavy to work.

We'd been journeying for months. We'd traveled by ship, steamer, canoe, and oxcart. We had trudged on foot. And this was what we'd come to. Tents, trash, and dirt.

"We better find a pile of gold to make up for living here," I grumbled.

Pa stood up and wiped his hands on his britches. He lifted one arm upward.

"Quit looking on the ground, son," he said. "Raise your eyes to the heavens!"

I looked up to where the mountains towered over us. As Pa and I watched, the sun started to set over the peaks. The sky turned a wonderful rosy color. The light trapped in the cracks of the mountains gleamed.

"I reckon not all the gold in California is in the ground," Pa said.

I had to admit he was right.

Chapter

Working Our Claim

Pa and I awoke at dawn. We dressed in dark pants and flannel shirts. We pulled on sturdy boots. We clapped broad-brimmed hats on our heads.

Pa cooked breakfast over an open fire. Again we ate bacon, beans, and bread. We washed everything down with a big cup of coffee.

Then we headed to our **claim**. It was about five square miles.

Whenever we weren't working our claim, Pa left his hat there. By leaving it behind, we showed the other miners the land was taken.

Shirttail Hill was a ragged place. But the miners did try to keep some order.

Town officers were elected. A town code was set up.

The code stated how big each miner's claim could be. It also protected

Town code

the miners against *claim jumpers*. Those were men who tried to take over other men's diggings.

Pa and I and the other miners spent all day at our claims. We searched for *placer*, or surface, gold. It was in the form of dust, flakes, or nuggets.

The first forty-niners dug through the gravel at the bottom of dried-up riverbeds. They put their findings on blankets and tossed them in the air. The lighter dirt would blow away. The heavier gold would stay on the blanket. This was called *dry washing for pay dirt.* But the miners soon learned they could find more gold using a washing pan. That's what Pa and I did.

We'd wade into the creek where the water was very deep. We'd fill our pans with gravel. We'd lower them into the creek.

Carefully, we'd swish the pans around. Then we'd tilt them to let the water and gravel run out. Any gold would stay in the bottom of the pan.

Miner panning for gold at edge of a stream

We panned for gold 12 hours a day. It was hard work. The water in the creek was icy. My bottom half would be freezing, while my top half broiled in the sun.

My back ached something fierce. So did my arms.

With each pan of dirt, I'd hope that this was the one. The big strike. The find that would make us rich. It was the same thing every miner in Shirttail Hill and all the other camps wished.

Then one day it happened. It was a morning just like all the rest.

Frogs sat sunning themselves on nearby rocks. Bugs skimmed over the water. Butterflies floated by. Minnows darted between my legs.

The only difference was that on that day I found a nugget in the bottom of my pan!

"I did it!" I cried out. "Gold!"

Pa sloshed over to me. He picked up the nugget. **"Eureka!"** he shouted. "You sure did do it, son!"

I forgot my sunburned face and my icy legs. I forgot my aching back. I'd found gold!

5 Chapter

A Day Off

Life in Shirttail Hill was rugged. But all the miners were friendly. We all helped one another. If a man borrowed a pan, pick, or shovel, he always returned it.

We all dressed the same and ate the same bad food. We worked the same long, hard hours. We slept in the same uncomfortable tents.

It didn't matter if someone had been rich or poor back in the States. It didn't matter what kind of job he'd had. And it certainly didn't matter what kind of house he'd lived in. In the mining camps, everyone was equal.

On Sunday, we all took the day off from mining.

That was the day we did our chores. I chopped wood. Pa hung out our bedding. He washed our clothes. Sunday was also the day we took our weekly bath.

At night, we sewed up the holes in our pants and shirts. Then we rubbed bear grease on our boots to keep the water out.

Miners resting on Sunday

Lots of the miners headed for the saloon on Sundays. They drank whiskey. And they played cards and rolled dice.

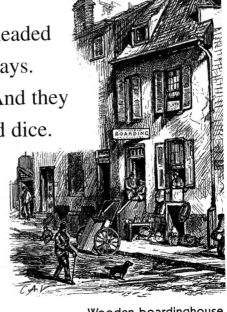

Pa was dead set against gambling.

"I work too hard for my money to throw it away," he always said. "Many a

Wooden boardinghouse

miner leaves the saloon with empty pockets."

On Sundays, Pa and I went to the **boardinghouse** for a good meal. At least it was a better meal than the ones we ate during the week.

Many men crowded into the double-wide tent. We sat elbow-to-elbow at a long wooden table.

We'd feast on potatoes, beans with molasses, and sometimes squirrel or rabbit stew. The meal always ended with **vinegar-and-sugar pie** or apple pie made without apples.

Wrestling matches and footraces were held on Sunday afternoons. Sometimes we had horse or mule races and rat races too. Lots of the miners bet on these contests.

Some Sunday nights there were even dances in the camp.

We'd all head to the boardinghouse. The musicians would plunk out "Oh, Susannah!" or "Camptown Races" on banjos, harmonicas, and fiddles.

Banjo

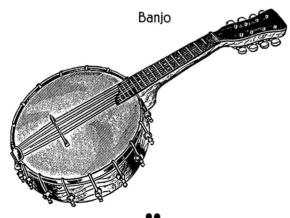

Half of the men would tie bandannas around their arms. That marked them as women. Then everyone would grab a partner and off we'd go.

It was sure a funny sight to see one big, bearded miner swing another big, bearded miner in a do-si-do.

Gals were mighty scarce in the gold camps. In fact, there wasn't one woman in all of Shirttail Hill. There wasn't a woman for a hundred miles in any direction!

One day, one of the miners in our camp set up a lady's bonnet and boots in the boardinghouse. He charged a dollar for one look. The men were so desperate to see something girlie, they paid the dollar!

The last thing Pa and I did on Sunday was write a letter to Ma and Mary Jane.

It was the only night we weren't too tired to pick up a pencil.

Chapter

A Little More Time

At least once a week, a miner would leave Shirttail Hill.

"I'm going back to the States," he'd say. "I've had a bellyful of gold mining."

But no matter how many men left, more always showed up to take their places.

Then summer turned to autumn. I started to get mighty sick of mining myself.

One night, I just blurted it out.

"Pa," I said, "I think we should go home. We're not making as much money as we thought we would."

"That's true," Pa said.

The amount of gold dust a man could hold between his thumb and forefinger was equal to $1. On good days, Pa and I made $20. It seemed like a fortune.

Back home, most men made about a dollar a day.

Everything in camp cost a huge amount of money. Most of the local farmers and ranchers had run off to the goldfields. Their crops hadn't been replanted.

Supplies were carried over the mountains by mule trains. That meant food and supplies cost even more than they did in San Francisco.

A slice of bread was $1. An egg could cost as much as $3. But we had to eat.

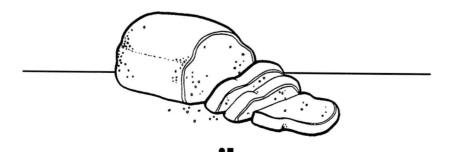

"I know what I'll do," Pa said. "I'll buy a rocker."

A *rocker* was a long box set on rockers like those on rocking chairs. Metal spikes called *cleats* were fastened to the bottom of the rocker.

Gold mining in California

One miner would shovel dirt onto the top tray. The tray was full of little holes.

The second miner would pour in water. That sent the dirt flowing through the box. The gold was supposed to fall to the bottom and catch on the cleats.

"With a rocker, we'll be able to wash for more gold than with our pans," Pa said. "And we won't have to stand in the water all day. Let's give it a try. I have a feeling our luck is gonna change soon."

"That's what all the men say," I grumbled. " 'Give it another day, another week.' "

"Our luck is bound to change!" Pa said again.

I stood up. I kicked the toe of one boot against the barrel Pa was sitting on.

"I think we've given it all the time we ought to," I said.

Pa snapped his suspenders.

"Simmer down, Andy," he said. "I'm gonna tell you a little story I heard yesterday."

I sat back down on my box and folded my arms. Pa went on.

"It seems this miner was mighty tired of **prospecting**. Just about as tired as you, I reckon. But his partner wouldn't give up. So they kept on.

"Well," Pa continued. "One morning his partner just up and died. The first miner decided that just as soon as he was done burying his partner, he'd head back home."

Pa looked at me, his eyes twinkled.

"Wouldn't you know it?" he said. "In the hole the miner had dug to bury his partner was the biggest gold nugget he'd ever seen."

Pa paused before continuing. "Now that miner's living the good life in San Francisco!"

In spite of myself, I laughed out loud at Pa's story. "That's a tall tale. And you know it!" I laughed.

"Sure it is," Pa answered. "But what I'm trying to say is, I'm homesick and tuckered out too. But I think we should stick it out a little longer."

Miners going back to the States

Chapter 7

Winter

Autumn faded. Winter set in. Many of the miners headed to San Francisco to wait out the cold weather.

Pa said we'd save more money by staying put.

But soon the days started to get mighty raw and mighty wet. The rain came down in buckets.

Those of us left in camp couldn't work our claims. We couldn't even walk. We would lose our boots in the squishy mud.

Our tents got soaked during the day.
They froze up cold as ice at night. Rivers
and creeks overflowed their banks.

Miners traveling in the rain

Mule trains stopped coming into the mountains. We were running out of food.

Pa went hunting one day. I went out the next. Whatever we shot, we shared with the others. We all shared whatever we had.

Pa bought a cookstove. We huddled around it, trying to stay warm.

Christmas that year was pretty sad. There were no presents. No Christmas tree glowed with candles. Worst of all, Ma and Mary Jane weren't there.

Our one treat was a tin of canned peaches.

Some of us did get together at the boardinghouse to sing carols. But that just made me feel worse.

A few weeks after Christmas, we had a terrible storm. Lightning cut the sky. Thunder roared. Our tent shook in the fierce wind.

The next morning, Pa woke up sick. Deep coughs shook his body.

I took care of him. I tried to remember all the things Ma had done when one of us was ill.

I spooned warm soup down Pa's throat. I sponged his face when his fever got bad. When the chills came, I covered him with blankets.

Heaps of other men had come down sick. It wasn't surprising. The weather was freezing.

Our flour was full of weevils. When we couldn't hunt, we ate rotten meat. We hadn't had any real fruit or vegetables since coming to the camp.

Some of the sick men got better. Some of them didn't. The graveyard at Shirttail Hill filled up. But I was determined that no one would dig a hole in the hard ground for my pa!

I ran to the boardinghouse. My teeth were chattering when I got there. My eyelashes were frosted over

"My pa is real sick," I gasped. "Do you have something—anything—that might help him?"

The man who ran the boardinghouse was The Gent. Gent was short for "gentleman."

The Gent got his name because he took two baths a week. He also kept his beard trimmed and his hair neat.

"You got any bear grease?" The Gent asked me. I nodded my head.

"Rub the grease all over your pa's chest," the Gent said. "Lay it on thick. Then put a warm blanket over that."

I blinked in surprise. Was The Gent pulling my leg? "We use bear grease on our boots," I said.

"I know, son." The Gent smiled. He ran both his hands over his oily, black hair. "But once, I was really sick. An Indian saved my life with bear grease. He did for me just what I'm telling you to do for your pa.

"Since then, I've used bear grease for whatever ails me," The Gent said.

I was so worried about Pa, I'd try anything. I ran back to our tent.

I followed The Gent's orders. Sure enough, the next morning, Pa started feeling better!

I was mighty glad to see Pa back to his old self. But I have to say, that bear grease had the worst smell that ever went up a man's nose.

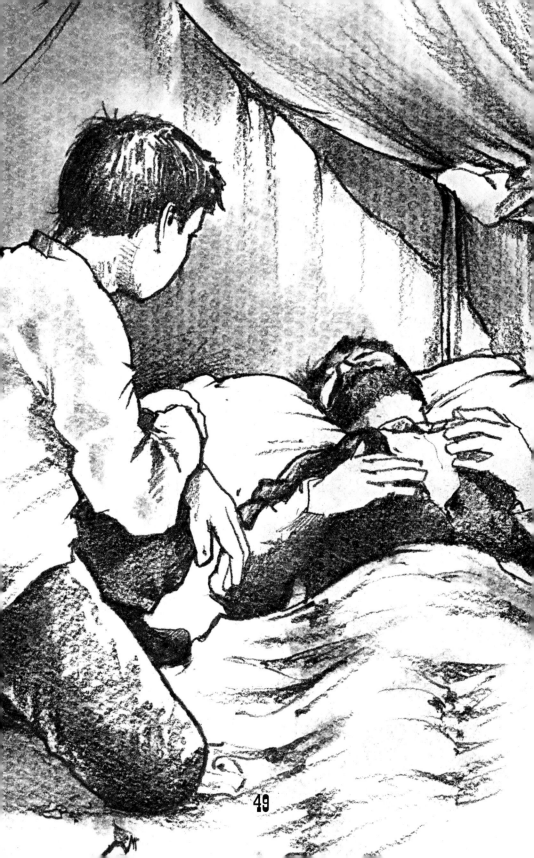

Chapter 8

Good News

The mountain oaks started putting on their greenery. The world turned warm and fresh again. Wildflowers bloomed. I took off my woolen **long johns**.

One morning we were eating our beans and bread. Pa looked up and said, "I reckon it's time we started building a cabin."

I stared at him. "What did you say?"

"I think we should build it farther up the hill," Pa went on. "I think we should plant some flowers too. Ma would like that."

"Ma?" I echoed. "What do you mean?"

Pa grinned at me. "I counted up our gold last night. I figure we've got enough to send for Ma and Mary Jane. Enough to build us a proper house too."

I couldn't believe it. I wanted to jump up for joy and do a dance. Pa looked like he did too. He clapped me on the back.

"We'll head down to San Francisco today," Pa said. "We'll get our gold weighed and changed into money. And then we'll get us a room in a hotel!"

"You mean, we're gonna sleep in a real bed?" I asked.

"You bet," Pa answered. "And eat a real meal. We'll even take a bath in a real bathtub. What do you say to that?"

I was too happy to say anything.

Chapter

Afterword

After the first year of the gold rush, things started to change in the mining camps. Women joined their men. Churches and schools were built.

Many of the miners stopped looking for gold and planted crops instead. Or they opened businesses.

Some of the camps became real communities. Others turned into ghost towns.

California became a state in 1850.

California state seal

After California became a state, John
Sutter discovered he had no legal claim to
his property. His workers deserted him.

Miners tore up Sutter's land with picks
and shovels. Others got rich, but John Sutter
was ruined.

View of Jamestown, California, south mines

Levi Strauss came to the gold camps to sell tent canvas. But he soon saw the miners had a greater need for sturdy pants. And so he created Levi blue jeans.

James Marshall, the man who first found gold, tried mining for a while. He was never successful.

Even though Pa and Andy Farrell are not real people, their story is real. The things Andy tells about are exactly what happened to the forty-niners who rushed West to hunt for gold.

What do you think happened to the Farrells—Pa, Ma, Andy, and Mary Jane?

I'd like to think they lived long and happy lives in the golden hills of California.

Glossary

boardinghouse   place where people pay to sleep and eat

claim   piece of land that a person takes as his or her own

eureka   Greek word, meaning "I have found it."

flour mill   place where wheat is ground into flour

hodgepodge   jumbled mixture

land grant   government document giving land

long johns   long underwear

myth   traditional story that explains happenings or beliefs

nugget   solid lump of a precious metal

pantaloons	loose-fitting pants that are usually just above the ankles
prospecting	searching for precious metal
sawmill	place where logs are sawed into lumber
serape	colorful woolen shawl worn over the shoulders
steamer	ship propelled by steam
tall tale	exaggerated story
tannery	place where animal hides are turned into leather
to the gills	to the maximum
vinegar-and-sugar pie	dessert made with water, vinegar, eggs, lots of sugar, cornstarch, and a lump of fat; then baked between two pie crusts
warehouse	place where supplies are stored